THE WORLD STARE-OUT CHAMPIONSHIP FINAL

PAUL HATCHER

BLOOMSBURY

First published 1999
Copyright © Paul Hatcher 1999

The moral right of the author has been asserted

Bloomsbury Publishing Plc, 38 Soho Square, London, W1V 5DF

A CIP catalogue record for this book
is available from the British Library

ISBN 0 7475 4507 3

10 9 8 7 6 5 4 3 2 1

Printed in Hong Kong by South China Printing Co.

For Mum and Dad

Thanks to:

Charles Rainey and Robert Hatcher (original patrons)

Rory Little, Aengus Little, Caroline Harris, Gosh Comics (39 Great Russell Street, London WC1B 3PH), Graham Linehan and Arthur Mathews, Chris Shepard, Talkback Productions and Assorted Images

Special thanks to:

Paul Hillery, Aleen Toroyan, Norman Hathaway, Karin Wichert, Jo Hilton and Kasper de Graaf

...and we talk about the *natural ability* of stare-masters, but my goodness Kampagnola's working hard out there! You can just feel the pressure that the Italian is applying to Nanak *and what an attack he's lining up here! Kampagnola is really starting to*

turn the screw and he's pinning the Indian to his chair! This is **very aggressive stuff** *from the Italian! Kampagnola's going up a gear,* **and I think he's got the Indian worried! Surely this championship can't spring any more shock results on us!!**

But Alessandro Kampagnola is producing some of the best stare-out I've ever seen! *And just take look at that expression on Nanak's face! He's in* **big, big trouble** *now and he's fading fast!! But it's Kampagnola! It's* **still** *Kampagnola!!* **And it's still**

Kampagnola!!! *...And Italy's Alessandro Kampagnola has sensationally blasted India's Anand Nanak out of the World Championship and just look at the jubilation on the Italian's face!! He's into his first World Final! Fantastic stare-out!*

Hello and welcome to the programme... Yes it's *Alessandro Kampagnola* against *Sigmund Spassky* in this afternoon's *World Stare-out Championship Final*, a

Alan Redfern

major achievement for both of these players. Kampagnola's *incredible* run of form makes him the *first ever* Italian to reach the final stage of the World

Championship, and we'll be seeing what sort of preparations he's been making over the last couple of days...

...my staring is going well... and I am looking forward to play against Sigmund, and to enjoy the game...

...and Poland's *Sigmund Spassky* could today become the first ever stare-master in the history of the game to take the *World Title* for a record breaking *seventh*

time. Spassky tells us his thoughts and feelings about the defence of his title and he also tells us what he thinks of his opponent in today's match...

...two years ago Alessandro was staring well... but he was not getting the results or recognition he deserved...

Duff Morgan speaks to Sigmund Spassky. We also have highlights of this morning's match for third place between the two losing semi-finalists, India's *Anand Nanak*

and former world champion, Russia's *Yuri Uzlian*... and as always we have plenty of analysis from our two *resident experts* former *English National Champion* and

current *Secretary to The Federation of British Stare-Masters*, *John Wilkinson,* and joining John is the current holder of the *United States National Indoor Stare-*

Out Trophy and *American Number One, Samuel Wallace*... but the man currently grabbing all the media attention is Italian stare-master *Alessandro Kampagnola,*

and the question on everybody's lips is can he beat the world champion? We sent *Ray Landau* to find out...

Alessandro, you're the first Italian and only the second non-seeded player ever to reach a world final, how have you been handling all the media attention?

Well it is to be expected, all professional stare-master come here to play and to win all their game, er... and to win the title, so they should not be surprised if

they stare well... it is this that all masters want to do and I, er... I always believe in myself and I knew that I can stare-out the best in the world...

You're a player that's been professional for nineteen years now, why do you think it is that you are finding your best form at 40?

I think many many reason... I have a new trainer, er... *Augusto Luigi*, who has been wonderful for me and he has give me the right training technique... my mind is very

strong and, er... much more *focus* and I also start to take relaxation session. I am in *good* health both mentally and, er... *physically*, so I play well...

You've always been a very popular stare-master and had a huge following over the years, what sort of reward is this for all your fans?

Yes my fans always support me, er... and sure, they are looking forward to the final. I am pleased to be able to give this to my fans, I, er... I do this for them and to win

the title for my country would be fantastic and, er... good for Italian stare-out too, as football is still the national game.

...I know that Anand was *attacking very aggressively* and, er... *certainly* in the early part of the game he was in front, but I focus well... and *fight these moments in*

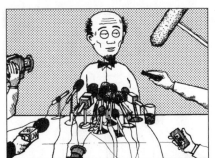

the match to *hold on*... but soon after... I don't know, maybe, er... 50 minutes, I chose the right moment to attack to try to finish the match... and luckily I did...

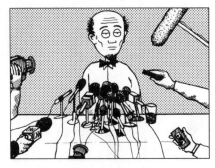

Alessandro!- *Alessandro? You-*

How do you feel about-

Alessandro?-

Hey Al! Well done man-

What will you?-

After the semi-final you said that you deliberately tried to finish the game, have you been developing a more attacking style of play?

Er... yes. Augusto felt that I was a strong player in defending but that I need to be a more, er... *aggressive starer*, so I train hard and have my sparring partner *Pablo*

Andriotti defend against me more, so that I can, er... *attack and counter attack* in matches. I also keep my back straight and sit up in the chair more.

Nanak said after the match that you out-witted him tactically...

He said this? Thank you Anand! Of course he was expected to win this game as the favourite, and so I try to surprise him with my play. Anand started very well

but, er... I take the opportunities in the match and held on to this advantage to win the game. I play with much variation in my staring and, er... I play well...

And Kampagnola certainly has been playing well, breezing through the quarter final against the much fancied and in form Jamaican youngster *Lloyd Obidiah*, who played with some very interesting tactics, but seemed to just fall away after a gruelling

two hours and forty-five minutes against Kampagnola. Obidiah later blamed the defeat on a small lapse in concentration at a crucial stage in the match. This left the Italian through to the semi-final with another tough match, this time against the third

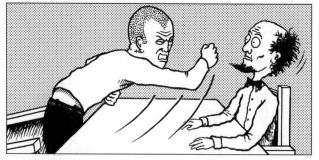

seed Anand Nanak who had himself had been producing some great stare-out. But surprisingly it was the underdog that proved to be the stronger of the two as Nanak crumbled to a superbly orchestrated counter attack. However, it was still Kampagnola's

controversial third-round match that provided the major talking points, when Ireland's hard man of stare-out *Seamus Rafferty* threw a wild punch. The world number four was immediately disqualified and the match awarded to Kampagnola.

Alessandro, you've had some wonderful results getting to the final, but everyone is still talking about the third-round match between yourself and Seamus Rafferty...

Sure, it is sad that Seamus gets so much attention because, er... the game was a good one, and it was unfortunate for it to end in this way...

No one doubts that Seamus Rafferty is a great player but how do you feel about his attack on you? Surely it's not what we want to see encouraged in the game?

Er, sure no, but er... stare-out is a very competitive sport and it can produce many passions, and, er... if the match is a tense one, then these passions can

maybe take over. I feel, er... *sorry* for Seamus because maybe sometimes the crowd want him to be like this but, er... he is quite young and so he will learn to deal

with this I am sure. I hope he will be back to, er... to play stare-out very soon. These things happen in stare-out. It is sad.

Well the final is tomorrow, how have you been preparing yourself? You must be a bit nervous?

Of course yes, a bit nervous, but I feel good to play the final, my staring is going well... and I am looking forward to play against Sigmund, and to enjoy the game.

Spassky's never been out-stared, he's in line for an unprecedented seventh title, it isn't going to be an easy match for you Alessandro is it?

It isn't going to be easy of course, but I know that Sigmund is not invincible and that he must, er... *lose* a stare-out match sometime, maybe tomorrow?

Thanks for talking to us Alessandro and good luck in the final.

Thank you Ray.

He's certainly handling the pressure well Kampagnola, isn't he gentlemen?

He's handling it very well and he seems to be genuinely relaxed... Luigi will have told him how important it is not to show any signs of weakness before the match,

but even so, it's still surprising to see how well he's adjusted to the top level and it's good to see him in such a positive frame of mind. I think his tough mental atitude is

one of the things that really helped him to dominate in the semi-final. Kampagnola's counter-attacking strategy was simply breathtaking...

Confidence is the name of the game, you know Alan? All of the success and the media attention doesn't seem to have gone to Alessandro's head and it would

be fatal for him to be overconfident, but he seems to still have his feet firmly on the ground despite riding high after his magnificent results, you know?

It was certainly a tremendous victory in the semi-final against Nanak John, you attended the match, just *how good* is this man Kampagnola?

He's already proved what a tremendous player he is with victories against players like Japan's *Chikamatsu Konishiki* and Canada's *Roland Pill*, after the semi-final

even Nanak had to acknowledge that Kampagnola had out-played him and it certainly isn't a fluke beating a man of Nanak's stature.

But by any standards this has been an amazing championship for Kampagnola, what's produced this sudden fantastic run of form Sam?

Alessandro has always been the nearly man and he's been proving very resilient against a lot of the top players. In the South American Open last year he put in

a very impressive performance against me, but up to now he just hadn't been able to turn good performances into good results, you know?

He said in the report that concentrating on attacking stare-out has really helped his game, do you think that he's now got the balance right?

His game has been totally revitalised and you can tell how secure he's feeling at the moment Alan, but I know Alessandro won't feel over-confident or cocky about

the big wins he's had so far, you know? The way he is handling the pressure both on and off the stare-table is wonderful to see...

What about that incident with Rafferty in round three John? Kampagnola didn't even blink - that is surely the sign of a *great player* isn't it?

I must admit that I'm rather surprised how gracious Alessandro was to Rafferty, it's that sort of attack that could potentially end the career of any professional stare-

master, and Kampagnola could easily have sustained an injury that might have been serious enough to keep him out for the rest of the season...

I think it's obvious that Alessandro didn't want to get embroiled in the controversy surrounding Rafferty, you know? I think he also feels a bit sorry for the young

Irishman as it's now his second lengthy suspension and I know his huge American following were very disappointed to see him disqualified in that way because he's

usually such an exciting player to watch you know? His four month suspension and £95,000 fine will hopefully give him time to work on his temperament...

I think it's worth adding that it could have easily been Rafferty in today's final if the Irish youngster had just been able to maintain a bit more control...

Gentlemen, thank you. Well earlier today the small matter of third and fourth place still had to be decided between Anand Nanak and the other losing semi-finalist,

Yuri Uzlian. Here's *Terry Fuller* with the highlights...

There was plenty of media speculation before this game that it was going to be a dull affair, that was the predicted script and these two players stuck to it. With the real prize of a place in the World Final gone, it only remained for both *Anand Nanak* and *Yuri Uzlian* to pick themselves up and stare for third place. Nanak started with his usual intense opening but then just sat defensively staring. This seemed to suit an equally defensive Uzlian and so it was a bit of creativity, a bit of stare-out magic

that was needed to break the deadlock, but with both players seemingly content to sit out, rather than to stare-out, it was not looking like an opening would come. Nanak, favourite in next week's Asian Five Nations Trophy, appeared determined just to keep himself fit and injury free, and it can only be speculated that the 73,519 crowd were unable to get tickets for the Final and had to make do with third place seats. After this performance they probably wished they hadn't bothered and apart from the

odd subtle move, Uzlian didn't produce any of the form that saw him to two World Titles. It was time to wheel out the old clichés, things could only get better, but they didn't. Many fans were already starting to leave the ground, when Nanak, always the

hungrier of the two stare-masters, stole the initiative after 1 hour and 17 minutes, and Russia's Yuri Uzlian ended up second best for the second time in two days. It was relief for the crowd and players alike...

Not an entirely enthralling game, and not really that surprising either Sam?

No not surprising Alan, you know? Both players will have realised that they are tying up the loose ends, but it's still a shame for the spectators...

Third in the world by anyone's standards isn't a bad achievement John, but Uzlian disappointed today didn't he?

He's not had the greatest of seasons by his high standards. It's now been over a year since Uzlian last won a major title and I think this game was a reflection of

that. As the match progressed it became very clear that the last two weeks of *tough, intensive stare-out* has taken its toll on both of these stare-masters. But

still, Nanak's done a terrific job and you have to give him credit for winning, and I think that if he'd been offered third place at the beginning of the championship

then he'd probably have settled for that.

Well it's certainly been a good season for Anand Nanak and yesterday evening at the annual Stare-out Awards in London, he won the prestigious *Stare-master of*

the Year Golden Eyeball, and there he is collecting the eyeball from the *President of The World Stare-out Association, Ference Hidegkuti*, and the award was in

recognition of his steady rise up the world rankings over the last two years as well as for his three major titles, and now third in the world ...so well done Anand...

...and the *Lifetime's Achievement Award in Stare-out* went to an absent *Sid Hartha* for contributing of over fifty years to the sport. His long career has seen him win

over *seventy titles* including six World Championships... and so congratulations also to the veteran Tibetan...

...okay...

...well it's been quite some time since the World Champion Sigmund Spassky last gave a televised interview but *Duff Morgan* caught up with him at his Park

Lane apartment yesterday to find out his views on defending his title as well as his thoughts on the current state of British stare-out...

Sigmund you're in the final for an unprecedented seventh time now. It's business as usual for you, isn't it?

...I am happy to be in the final...

There's been much speculation in the papers that you're playing your best ever stare-out, how do you feel about that? How do you currently rate your game?

...my game is good... but I am always looking to improve... the important thing is to learn from each match... each game must always be a learning experience...

If you win your seventh title tomorrow, you'll break the record you hold jointly with Tibet's Sid Hartha, what will that mean to you?

...my aim tomorrow is to win the title... I see records as a bonus...

You came through some pretty tough rounds, but we were all surprised how well our own Jonathan Cauldwell did against you in Round 2 lasting forty-three minutes, it made something of a national hero out of him...

...he played well... he had a good temperament... the crowd was behind him... that helped with his performance...

This year's championship has had plenty of upsets, how close was Cauldwell to winning and why do you think that he managed to do so well against you?

...although Caudwell played well... the match was not out of my control... I never felt threatened...

I just want to ask you about the current state of English stare-out, how do think the future looks for us?

...you have some interesting prospects... Cauldwell will improve... but you are a long way from producing a champion... you have some potential at under 15's level...

Richard Pierce... John Whitaker... Jo Vaughan... all good to watch... Johnny Macgill has done some very good work at The Sir Gerald Langstone-Moore School

of English Stare-out... the school is the future for English staring...

You took on American Stare-Master Ted Stead in the quarter-finals and then went on to play against former world champion Yuri Uzlian in the semi's, not an easy run-in to the final by any standards?

...Stead was disappointing... he was edgy... it was an easy match for me to win... Stead can play better...

...Uzlian stared well... he played the opening half hour at a fast pace... I was very impressed with Uzlian... holding on for five minutes against me with just one eye was an achievement... as opening it would have meant instant disqualification... after I had

soaked up his attacks... and his initial pressurising... I knew I would win...

What about Alessandro Kampagnola? We know that you've been friends for many years now, but how do you rate him as a player?

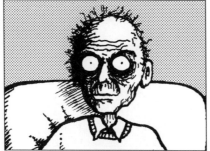

...I am not surprised that he is in this year's final... two years ago Alessandro was staring well... but was not getting the results or the recognition he deserved...

...he has been training hard... he's a man that can handle a world final...

And how *do* you rate his chances against you in the final?

...he has more chance than Uzlian.

An usually candid Spassky speaking to Duff Morgan there... John, all the sensible money's on Spassky isn't it?

I honestly don't think that Kampagnola *does* have much more of a chance than Uzlian! I can't see this one going any other way Alan, you could see from the

clips that Spassky's in superb form, he disposed of *both* Stead and Uzlian and didn't even break into a sweat! Spassky's composed, focused, he can take any

amount of pressure and he doesn't give away chances. If he has got an Achilles heal, then Kampagnola's going to have a tough time finding it!

Spassky seems to be taking everything in his stride Sam, how do think he'll approach the final against Kampagnola?

I don't think he needs to change anything from his winning formula, you know? Like John says, he's been playing some great stare-out and he's been *totally committed*

throughout the championship, but it will certainly be interesting to see what sort of approach Alessandro has. It was very interesting to hear what Sigmund had to

say about British stare-out Alan. Andy Dudley is certainly worth mentioning too. He was very unlucky to be disqualified against *Ion Drimba* in Round 2...

Well I can tell you that Dudley had his appeal against his disqualification for movement abuse turned down by the Stare-out Association. Dudley said he'd

now concentrate on the qualifying heats for the European Championships in Bonn later this year... and one other item of news is that the Ukrainian Stare-master

Roman Solowka has announced that he is retiring from the game at the age of 62. Solowka, who was defeated in Round 1 by Yuri Uzlian, said he was very sorry to be leaving the game after 45 years. A date for his testimonial match has yet to be announced... Now before we go over live to North Park Stadium and to this afternoon's final, we can quickly show you the result of our *Stare-out of the Championship* competition again, as chosen by our two experts here...

 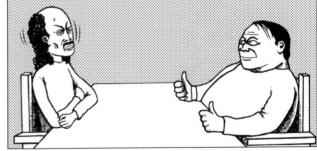

...no two ways about it, Frenkeva is dominating this game now, as we see the initiative see-saw once again and this time it's towards the Bulgarian! What a game this is! **Surely** *Frenkeva can't pull this one out of the bag?! He was down and out just* five minutes ago! **And Matasaki is clearly wavering now and yes, there he goes!! Frenkeva gets the thumbs up and does the impossible, turning this match round in just over 6 hours and 17 minutes and that was breathtaking stare-out!!**

E Matazaki (*Jap*) v **FRENKEVA** (*Bul*) Round 3
J de Couberin (*Fra*) v **SANDERS** (*USA*) Round 5
A **SPASSKY** (*Pol*) v Chan (*Chi*) Round 1

The World Stare-out Championship Final

Mrs **Edwina Stanton**, Devizes

The World Stare-out Championship Final

Breathtaking stuff indeed from one of the best, and so far the longest match of the Championship, Matazaki against Zlolt in Round 3. So the correct order once again was... *E, J, A*... that's *Zlolt Frenkeva, Quincey Sanders, Sigmund Spassky*... and so

congratulations again to Mrs Edwina Stanton who should have received a pair of tickets for today's final and I'm sure she's taken up her seat... and I'm just hearing that Spassky and Kampagnola are taking up their seats too, so we're going over

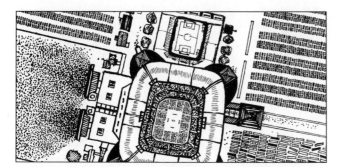

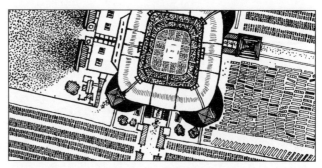

live now to the North Park Stadium and to this afternoon's match commentators, *David Joyce* and *John Barrington*...

Thank you Alan, and there you can see the spectacular aerial view of this magnificent North Park Stadium and I can tell you that the atmosphere here is *absolutely electric!* And just look at all those cars and coaches to the right of your picture, many

Match Commentators
David Joyce and John Barrington

fans have travelled from all over the country to be here for this historic World Final, and those who haven't got tickets can still watch the match on those enormous screens outside North Park which cater for the *mass of fans* that love come to the

World Final despite not having tickets... and there's the Stare-out balloon, giving us that *marvellous* bird's eye view of North Park and it's a perfect afternoon for stare-out, the forecast is a good one with sunny spells with a light southernly breeze and that

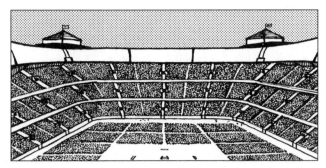

gives us virtually *perfect match conditions* here this afternoon... a real buzz of excitement there down at the Allen Road end of North Park and what a *marvellous* modern building this purpose built 200,000 seater stadium is for watching world stare-out...

Spassky and *Kampagnola*... just warming up... getting a few practice stares in and finding that all-important rhythm, just throwing across a few glances... Good Afternoon John, tell us, just how important is this warm-up session?

Well David, many past stare-masters have claimed that the match really starts as soon as the players leave the dressing rooms and meet in the entrance tunnel, so from a psychological point of view it's vital that neither player shows any sign of

nerves or weakness. It's also *very important* that both finalists warm the eye muscles up gently, easing into their respective styles and find that groove - the last thing either player will want is any small eyestrain...

Spassky won the toss and elected to stare from the Kempshott Road end and what a lovely appreciation of the game he has, even when just trying out a few basic moves, you can really *feel* the intensity... and Kampagnola's going to have deal with that in

this *the most important stare-out match of his life!* There's the third eye umpire *Jacob Mycroberg* on the left, and on the right of your picture, *Dr Daniel Scanlon*, the official timekeeper, just making some final preparations before the start of the match...

...and we've got a capacity crowd here, how good it is to see both sets of supporters mingling, enjoying the day out and just settling down for this afternoon's stare-out John?

Well all the effort that has gone into making stare-out a sport for all the family seems to have paid off David, and those minor crowd disturbances that we saw at the odd game a couple of years ago are hopefully a thing of the past now...

Yes, but it remains to be seen if stare-out *has* finally rid itself of that small hooligan element, and it was just a few... but we've had *great* crowds at all the world championship games so far and how good that is... Let's just see *Spassky's statistics*... that

Sigmund Spassky (*Pol*)

Age: **32**

World ranking: **1**
(Defending world champion)

Seeded: **1**

Career titles: **52**

The World Stare-out Championship Final

was rather a mouthful... Yes, *defending World Champion*, never been stared-out and so he remains the *undisputed World Number 1*... and he's the clear favourite today to retain his title for an incredible record breaking seventh successive year...

Alessandro Kampagnola (*Ita*)

Age: **40**
World ranking: **38**
Seeded: -
Career titles: **3**

The World Stare-out Championship Final

...and Kampagnola, ranked 38th in the world and unseeded for this championship... and it has to be said, a surprise finalist, not tipped by many to reach this stage, but a fantastic run of form has seen him reach his first-ever world final, certainly no fluke though, many of the top names have fallen to him and so I'm sure that he'll shoot up those world rankings and be seeded next year if he continues this fantastic form, but there's far more to this game than just statistics... as quiet starts to descend on

North Park... Chang Jin-ming, just checking his watch there, the players have had plenty of time to settle down now... and on the right, Chong Tsui-ju,today's match referee... just giving a signal over to Jacob Mycroberg that they're ready to begin and the crowd settled down in silence, anticipating the start of this year's *World Stare-out Championship Final* between the reigning champion, Sigmund Spassky and Alessandro Kampagnola... *And there it is! Jacob Mycroberg has blown his whistle!!*

And from the 256 players who started this championship, it's just about Sigmund Spassky and Alessandro Kampagnola now, as they lock together to contest for the ultimate title of World Stare Master... so both men with faces of iron... showing no

emotion and this is what it's all about, these two *stare gladiators* battling it out, both set on attaining that famous trophy, and just look how desperate Kampagnola is to win this title, he means business John!

Yes, and I think that everybody has been very impressed with Alessandro's recent form in this championship, and just taking a look at him now, he's very relaxed and composed... very good posture, and he doesn't look out of place at all David - you'd

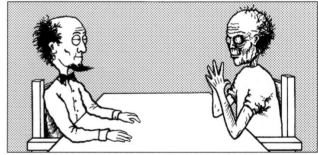

never guess that it's his first appearance in a major final and I must say that I'm very pleased for him...

Yes Kampagnola's made a lot of friends here, married of course, for eighteen years to his lovely English wife Karen, who's here in the crowd along with their two children, Gary, aged 16, and Tammy, aged 13. Karen doesn't usually like to

watch her husband's matches but she flew in yesterday, all the way from Pescara on the east coast of Italy specially for the final, and has taken her seat in the family enclosure in this packed stadium. And I'm informed that tickets for this final have

been changing hands for a phenomenal £4500 *each*, which just goes to show the sort of lengths people will go to witness this man Spassky in action, and I believe that the authorities have been trying to implement a crack-down on ticket-touts John?

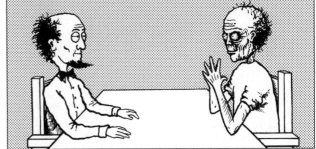

It was needed after the amount of forged tickets in circulation last year David, but I'm afraid the campaign hasn't been a total success and you can bet there are plenty of disappointed fans having to watch the match from outside the stadium...

...so both men still focusing on each other... both still looking fresh and relaxed, and Kampagnola will need to *weigh in* with *every ounce* of the experience that he's gained over the last twenty or so years as a professional Stare-Master if he's to

upset the form book here today... and so far he's looking like a man that knows what he's about with the extra finesse that's needed at this level, John?

Yes that's right. I've always believed that Kampagnola has had the potential to do damage, he's certainly a great battler, but he does sometimes get himself a little wound up against the top players... Spassky's phenomenal powers of concentration have

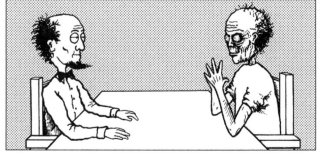

always impressed me, he plays to the narrowest of margins and is fiercely competitive, so Kampagnola will have to be wary of those devastating onslaughts if he is to have any chance at all today.

Well, there are plenty of people that say Spassky is *unbeaten* not *unbeatable,* and Kampagnola would love to be the man to defeat him... But it'll be very tough for the Italian out there today and the presence of mind that Spassky possesses is incredible.

Kampagnola is certainly going to have to improve on his past few performances against Spassky, twelve meetings and twelve defeats, all inside ten minutes, and the last time these two met was last year in the Chinese Open, where Kampagnola was

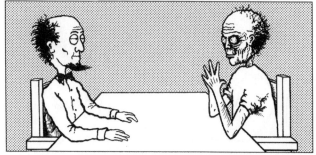

overwhelmed in just 3 minutes and 52 seconds, but you can bet your life that he would love to get his revenge here in this his first *World Final* and with his confidence riding high, you never know! Both these men though, always the best of friends,

except now in this packed stadium... but no doubt they'll remain the best of friends whatever the result is here today. And *still those eyes of steel try desperately to penetrate the opponent's defenses*... Kampagnola, as always, is immaculately dressed

with that distinctive lucky black bow tie and that light pink shirt, and I believe that the sale of black bow ties has rocketed in Italy since Kampagnola's success in this year's championship. You bought one John?

They're all sold out David!

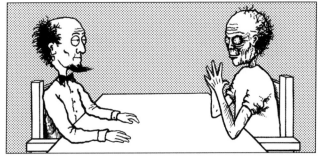

Ha Ha Ha! Yes it's amazing the commercial influence that the sport now has, Spassky in his famous short-sleeved sky-blue jumper, a jumper which is now the *biggest selling sportswear item ever*, much to the annoyance of Spassky himself, who

feels that fans are being taken advantage of by the excessive amounts that the sportswear companies charge for replica jumpers... but the *huge sea of blue* down at the Allen Road end is testimony to the high level of loyal support that Spassky now

has... very tense moments these... *crucial* part of the game this with neither player wanting to let their opponent in, both know they must maintain that *presence of mind*. Incredible to think John, that Spassky is the only stare-master on the circuit *not* to

have a team of advisers, a manager or personal trainer and although little is known about his training routine, it is known that it extensively involves the use of mirrors...

It's rumoured that he's actually managed to stare-out his own mirror image, David...

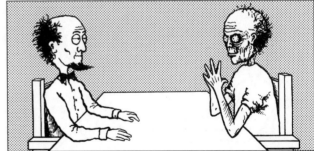

It wouldn't surprise me John! ...well, Spassky, a staunch vegan, considers his diet of uncooked natural foods such as nuts and berries, extremely important to keep in good shape and for him to maintain his trance-like state of staring... Kampagnola by way

of contrast has no specific diet as such and has a large team of advisers who, it has to be said, have done plenty of great work this season, especially during this tournament. Kampagnola's manager, *Augusto Luigi*, was telling me before the match that

he has been encouraging Kampagnola to have a few sessions with a hypnotist. John, your thoughts?

Well nothing new there - I must admit that I've always been rather sceptical of hypnosis, and I don't think it's added anything to the game at all, especially when you consider some of the mystical states that are achieved at this level... perhaps

Kampagnola thought it would help him get that vital first breakthrough...

Well it's certainly been intriguing stuff so far and at the moment things couldn't be tighter and *Oh! I don't believe It!* **Some head movement from Spassky!!** ... No... No... it won't count, someone in the crowd distracting him... So it remains all square, with

Kampagnola still holding out, matching Spassky stare for stare, and still keeping his sights set *firmly* on attaining that *Championship Crown*, not forgetting that winners cheque for £1,000,000, a handy little sum! And Kampagnola can rest

assured that he is at least guaranteed a runner-up cheque for £700,000, which would go some way to compensate him if he was to lose, but so far he's still in it... and the money of course, is secondary to actually winning the title...

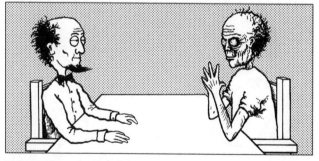

Talking of money David, it has to be said that the world number one's incredible dominance in the sport is matched only by his incredible generosity...

Yes, Spassky's generosity is as *renowned* as the man himself, and I believe that the *Great Olanov Children's Eye Hospital* in Spassky's home town of *Gdansk* received *a very considerable sum* said to be in the region of *a staggering £3,000,000!!*

Spassky has also made many other donations and investments for good causes, most notably his backing of the young Polish stare-masters of tomorrow, by setting up the *Polish Institute of Stare Excellence*... Kampagnola still maintaining a *real gritty*

determination and he's still really reading this match *superbly...* Spassky's phenomenal success has also inspired his home country of Poland to adopt staring as their national sport which can only be good for the game in general John?

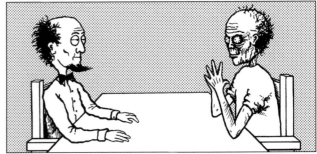

Well, with the players receiving more and more money from their sponsorship and broadcasting deals, particularly from satellite television companies, the more money that is actually reinvested at the grass roots of stare-out the better. Obviously

the large prize money on offer has attracted a lot of youngsters to the game, so the future looks good in that respect. But I do feel that the amount of money floating around is becoming just *too excessive*, and on the whole *isn't* being churned back into

the sport, we're seeing *more and more* vested interests coming in the form of managers, advisers and agents, as well as these huge great support teams that the players now have, many of whom are surely motivated by greed, and it puts the players

under even more pressure to perform well and sometimes the actual game can be lost amongst that... So yes, it's always nice to see the generosity of someone like Spassky within the game. However, I'd hate to see Poland *completely dominating* the

sport in the way that the United States did ten years ago and it would be great if the same investments could come into the less well established countries, such as our own David.

Well thought provoking comments there from the former English Stare-Master *John Barrington*, continuing the debate about the huge amount of money currently floating around in the sport, and the commercialisation of stare-out, a debate that I'm sure is

set to continue for a long time yet... and a full house here today as you would expect, the final sold out nearly six months before the championship started... still *no sign* of a breakthrough *from either player* and still *no sign* of either man *buckling under the*

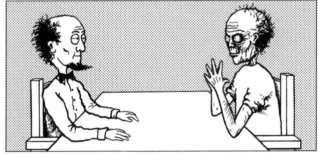

intense pressure... both these men still *matching each other in every respect*, and both these men with *minds like computers*, they know *exactly* what they can do and *exactly what they want to do* ...and I've always been an admirer of Spassky's sitting

position, shoulders tipped slightly forward, but counter balanced by his arm action, a great role model for any up and coming stare-master out there, and a good sitting position in stare-out is such a vital part of becoming one of the top level masters...

Latest: Man Utd 0 Leicester 2

...and just a few latest scores going through there, an important afternoon's action in the premiership and I believe that the Football Association has been complaining about the World Stare-out Championship Final being held today John?

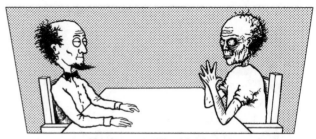

Chelsea 1 Wimbledon 1

Well teams like Manchester United usually command gates of 55,000 or so, but that falls to around 3000 on Stare-out Final day, which is a considerable drop in revenue for them and that just goes to show how popular stare-out is now David...

And looking at the action down there on the stare-table you can see why! Spassky forging ahead with hard powerful staring, but Kampagnola's still there, *battling* with a surge of stares and you can really feel the tension mounting in this stadium! And my

goodness the next few minutes are *really* going to take some watching... but Alessandro Kampagnola continues to fight and show the crowd that the gap between himself and the world number one means nothing to him...

You were talking about sitting positions a moment ago David and I think that Kampagnola's is interesting. It's a strong, solid stance, upright but almost laid back, defiantly relaxed... arms supportive but not taut, assertively laid out on the table as if

they're claiming territory, saying I'm in charge here... A couple of years ago he took his sitting position apart and rebuilt it after some advice from a certain *Sigmund Spassky* of all people, and since then there's *definitely* been a huge improvement in his -

Sorry to interrupt you John, but I think Kampagnola's starting to sweat! **Yes! There it is!!** *And the pressure starting to get to Kampagnola after what? 9 minutes!* John, we were both just saying how well Kampagnola was holding up!

Yes, Spassky *definitely* gaining the initiative there and it will be extremely important for Alessandro to *keep his concentration*, he'll know he's behind, but he's a *gutsy* campaigner and he'll most certainly have something left!

Let's just see that again now... *Yes definitely! There it is! A*nd you almost *expect Spassky* to produce *something special*, the ability of a *top player* to move up a gear John, especially at *this high level*...

That's right David! Spassky produced an attack from nowhere and when we were least expecting it and he's withstanding the pressure, pressure that Kampagnola won't be used to dealing with in a World Final...

Well it's not over yet! ...and it will be interesting to see how Kampagnola responds, he'll *know* that he'll have to produce an immediate reply. He's played *wonderfully up to now* but it's Spassky that takes that *commanding position!* So excitement

down on the stare table and excitement here in the commentary box as we received another cake this morning... in fact a lovely looking cake with some wonderful icing on the top in the shape of a wide staring eye! ...and *mmm*... yes... it's very, very nice!...

excuse me! The eye is actually made out of *...mmm...* the most *delicious* marzipan... so a very big thank you to a Mrs Elaine Howell of Taunton *...mmm...* yes, very tasty, John?

Thank you David! It's a real shame that the viewers can't see this cake because it really is quite magnificent... and *...mmm... yes...it's delicious!...* really quite exceptional! *...mmm...* and I must admit that... *I'm rather partial* to fruit cake... particularly

when it's as *exquisite as this one is*... so thank you very much indeed, Mrs Howell...

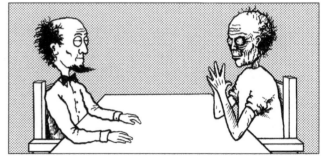

Yes do please keep your correspondence coming in and we'll endeavour to get through as much of it as we can... Anyway Kampagnola seems to have stabilised his position and has recovered well. He's looking pretty comfortable now so he

remains very much in this match... *mmm... delicious!*

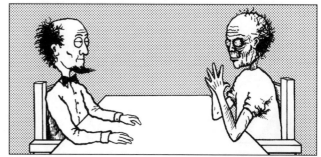

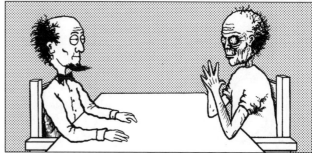

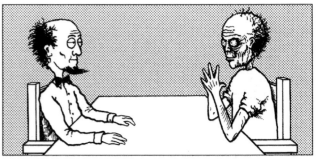

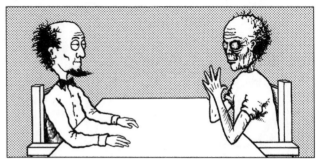

...intense concentration....

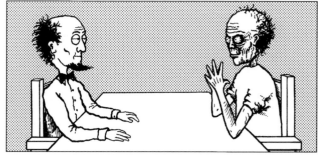

...and, er... we're being joined now in the commentary box by the reigning *Women's* World Stare-Master, *Natalie Grant!* Good afternoon Natalie...

Good afternoon David, good afternoon everybody...

Well Natalie, your comments so far, in particular on that first breakthrough from Spassky just a few minutes ago...

Well, I was expecting a breakthrough to come at around that stage of the game from Spassky, but I'm just hoping that Kampagnola can sit tight and come up with a reply and, like you said earlier, I think he'll have something left.

Well he certainly seems to have recovered his composure now, tell us Natalie what's the current situation on the women's front, things are moving in the right direction for the girls aren't they?

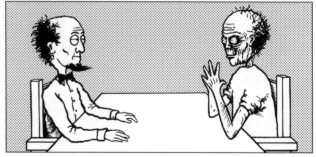

Yes that's right David, we've started attracting more interest in women's stare-out, so the future does look promising now and the girls are coming on really well, developing and improving their technique all the time...

Stare-out still very much dominated by the men in your opinion Natalie?

Yes it's unfortunate David, but I feel that the next ten years or so will see coverage of women's staring increase, particularly on terrestrial television which will hopefully help to bring in more young female players into the game. A lot of effort is being made

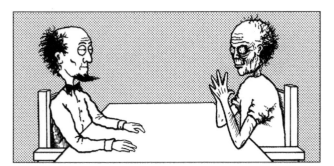

in schools to encourage girls to participate and start playing competitive stare-out. There are certainly a lot of girls who are getting involved now at that level and we've also been getting more and more semi-professional players joining W.A.S.M -

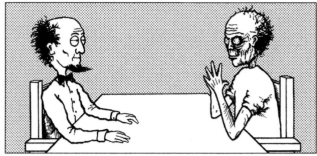

...The Women's Association of Stare-Masters...

...er yes... which should encourage more investment and then hopefully bigger prize money should follow, bringing us more into line with the men...

And it's good to see some female officials filtering into the sport too... Well thanks for coming in Natalie, and the best of luck next week in the Bognor Regis Challenge Cup...

Thank you David.

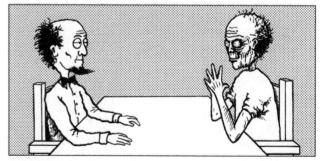

Whilst on the subject of officials John, they deserve a lot of the credit for such a successful championship this year. They've done an excellent job and I think that a special mention should go to *Chang Jin-ming* for all the hard work that he's put into

managing the championship and in particular the way that he and Chong Tsui-ju handled that incident in Round 3 involving Seamus Rafferty and Alessandro Kampagnola...

Yes, an unfortunate incident, and it could certainly have been a lot worse if it hadn't been for the prompt action taken by Chong Tsui-ju preventing some potentially very nasty scenes. It's just a shame that Rafferty can't quite seem to manage his temper,

and you would have thought that having just come back from suspension for testing positive for drugs, he would have learnt his lesson by now David...

Well, Rafferty is considered by many to be a real potential world champion, so it's unfortunate that he just can't seem to stay out of trouble and clean up his act. Drugs, of course, still such a real temptation for young impressionable stare-masters such as

Rafferty... and we seem to be seeing a real increase in their use, especially with the illegal application of eyedrops before the match, preventing the eyes from drying out, but it's encouraging to see the swift action being taken by the Stare-Out Association

in relation to this problem John, especially with the educational video that they've produced...

Yes, the video has gone some of the way to curb this worrying problem and it does seem to have had a genuine effect, but we can't afford to become complacent about the menace of drugs in the game, and I would guess that a lot of the problem lies in-

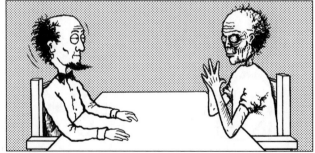

I'm going to have to stop you there John, because I think that we're seeing some more developments in the match! ***Yes!!*** ***Some head movement now from Kampagnola! Signs that his challenge may well be weakening. And he's in trouble!***

And Kampagnola's started to sweat again! And this will hurt Kampagnola! He'll know that he's down and the pressure now beginning to tell! *John, what are we seeing here?*

Well yes, Kampagnola definately starting to feel the heat and he'll be *desperate* to hang on, perhaps it's an indication of how tough he's finding it out there?

And Spassky's pummelling into Kampagnola, but the plucky Italian continues to hold on, absorbing the pressure, trying to take the sting out of Spassky's attack! Well maybe Kampagnola has finally overstretched himself John?

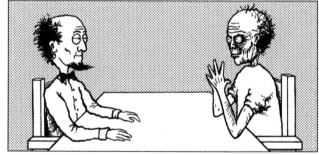

Spassky's shutting the door on him there David, *tightening* his *vice like grip* on this match, but credit to Kampagnola! He isn't giving up easily and maybe, just maybe, he still has something left in the reserves. He does seem to have stabilised his-

And more head movement from Kampagnola! Things really not looking good for the challenger as Spassky mounts **attack after attack** ...and what can Kampagnola do about this? You can see that he's *hanging on*, *trying to keep calm*, but he's

straining there... **and more sweating now!** Oh and it's all over now surely, it must be! John, anyway back for Kampagnola?

Well he's *certainly* in trouble David! He's *cracking* under the pressure, *definite head movements there and I can't see him pulling out of this, he's weakening fast now...* he's all over the place!

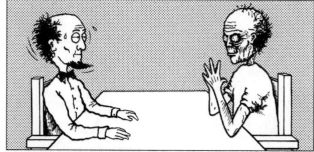

Spassky **pummelling** the Italian into submission, **unrelenting ruthless aggression** from Spassky, **tearing** into Kampagnola's tattered defences, **grinding his man down and showing no mercy!** Just how much longer can he last?! **Major problems**

here for Kampagnola! Look how **ungainly** he looks now... falling apart **piece by piece**, and **surely** this is just a formality now, he **must** be finished!! These are real **desperate** times for the Italian, and is **this intense match** nearing it's climax? But

what a great learning experience it's been for Kampagnola... **And his necks gone!! It must be all over now! He's come so far to the final, but stare-out can be such a cruel game!** John, Kampagnola will bounce back won't he?

He's played the game of his life David, and he's lasted just over 19 minutes so no disgrace at all, he's let nobody down and he can feel proud of the way that he's performed today. He'll be a better, more mature player from this experience. But let's not

take anything away from Sigmund Spassky! It's been a real honour to witness such a spectacular match as this, such true quality! Will this man ever be beaten?

Thank you John! *But **still** Kampagnola hangs on, trying to **claw his way back, but his way is barred by this immovable man Sigmund Spassky!** Surely he must know that he can't survive this, as he continues to go through **every emotion!** But both*

*these men have given us a wonderful exhibition of premier stare-out, and the Italian has worked so hard out there, you just **have** to feel for him... **And oh! They can't let this continue! Look at the agony on Kampagnola's face! Surely Spassky's***

***got the championship all wrapped up! He's re-writing the record books! Cramp simply must be setting in now for Kampagnola... AND LOOK AT HIM NOW! He's going down fighting! No! He must be finished!** Surely he has nothing*

left!! And the crowd are going wild, they think it's all over! IT IS NOW! KAMPAGNOLA HAS BLINKED!! YES! IT'S ALL OVER!! Spassky has masterfully retained the WORLD TITLE!! And what a CLASSIC FINAL this has been!!!

the end

A NOTE ON THE AUTHOR

Paul Hatcher began drawing comics in 1992, creating *The World Stare-Out Championship* two years later. He divides his time between developing his comics and writing sketches for TV. He lives in Northampton.

For further information send an SAE to:

House of Hatch
PO Box 476
Northampton
NN1 4ZX

www.stare-out.com